# The MindBody Workbook

## A Thirty Day Program Of Insight And Awareness
## For Back Pain And Other Disorders

## David Schechter, M.D.

This workbook was part of the treatment program for Dr. Schechter's TMS research study published in <u>Alternative Therapies</u>, Sept/Oct 2007.

MINDBODY
MEDICINE
PUBLICATIONS

# The MindBody Workbook

## A Thirty Day Program Of Insight And Awareness
## For Back Pain And Other Disorders

### David Schechter, M.D.

Minor text updates done October 2015, Feb. 2022

Research supports the use of expressive writing in certain types of arthritis and immune system problems. Individuals with irritable bowel syndrome, fibromyalgia, tension headaches, TMJ, chronic fatigue and anxiety also benefit greatly from this approach. (See "Recent Supportive Research" on page 13.)

**The MindBody Workbook**
**A thirty-day program of insight and awareness**
**for back pain and other disorders**

Published by:     MindBody Medicine Publications
                  mail to: 10811 Washington Blvd, Ste. 250
                  Culver City, CA 90232     www.MindBodyMedicine.com

Printed in the United States of America, in Los Angeles, CA.

Schechter, David
          MindBody Workbook/David Schechter, MD
          Includes bibliographical references and index.
          ISBN: 978-1-929997-00-8 (paperback)

©David Schechter, MD

| First Printing | November 1999 |
|---|---|
| Second Printing | January 2000 |
| Third Printing | July 2000 |
| ....... | |
| Thirteenth Printing | August 2013 |
| Fourteenth Printing | January 2015 |
| Fifteenth Printing | November 2015 |
| Sixteenth Printing | December 2016 |
| Seventeenth Printing | September 2017 |
| Eighteenth Printing | September 2018 |
| Nineteenth Printing | June 2019 |
| Twentieth Printing | August 2020 |
| Twenty First Printing | August 2021 |

**Warning—Disclaimer**
Anyone using this book for a medical condition should be under the care of a physician. The reader and his/her physician should decide appropriate use of this book in conjunction with usual and customary medical techniques and treatments. The reader should have appropriate medical examinations to diagnose his/her condition and exclude serious illnesses that may require immediate or aggressive treatment.

# Acknowledgments

I wish to thank my wife Lisa for her patience during my early morning and late evening retreats to the computer to write this manuscript. In addition, her devotion to our then infant son and her ability to keep him entertained while I worked on this Workbook helped immeasurably. Continued thanks and love to Lisa for all she does and who she is.

Deepest thanks to John Sarno, MD for teaching me to cure my knee pain and learn to help countless others with pain with his Tension Myositis Syndrome model of diagnosis and treatment. I also appreciate his referrals that began when we reconnected in the mid 1990's and helped me to develop my program of treatment in Los Angeles.

I must acknowledge the debt of gratitude I owe to George Engel, MD for the inspiration of the biopsychosocial model he developed and wrote about in the 1970's.

I wish to thank friends, colleagues, and patients who reviewed drafts of this work and offered comments and critiques. These include Annette Shaked, Roy Shaked, M.D., Stephen Lottenberg, M.D., Susan Mendenhall, David Nocenti, Donald Dubin, Heidi Solz, M.D., Lori Landau, and many others.

Thanks to all my current and recent staff as well—Vanessa, Kristina, Tina, Jessica, Lisa, etc. And prior staff including Sato, Jessica, and Aracely. I'd like to also thank my previous office team at LaCienega for their encouragement and support of my mindbody practice of medicine—Renee, Carlos, Ada, Giselle, Carlo, and Marzi. Also thanks to Hormoz Zahiri, MD for his encouragement.

I truly appreciate the opportunity to collaborate with psychotherapists who treat TMS most notably the late Donald Dubin, MFT, Arnold Bloch LCSW, Jessica Oifer, MFT, Justin Barker, Psy.D., and Samantha Bothast, LCSW.

It was a pleasure working with Arthur Smith, PhD on the research side of mind body medicine. It's crucial to have a partner with whom to flail at windmills.

Finally, and most of all, to all the patients who courageously break out of the model of "doctor cure me" and show the willingness to learn about the mindbody connection and the effort to work on these challenging issues to relieve their pain and improve their well-being.

# Table of Contents

# Introduction

Why a MindBody Workbook? Aren't there enough books describing and elaborating on the mind-body connection these days?

This Workbook is unique in that its design allows the interested and motivated reader to **make** the mindbody connection him or herself, not just read about it. The format is a "structured" journal that takes thirty days to complete. The use of a journal as part of a mindbody treatment program has been highly successful in my clinical practice in treating individuals with Tension Myositis (Myoneural) Syndrome (a common cause of chronic back pain) and other disorders (see page 10).

During the thirty days of this program, the active user of this workbook will respond to questions that I have found useful with many patients and gradually gain insight and awareness into the role that emotions may be playing in their illness or condition. The time required is not extensive (ten to twenty minutes a day) but commitment is required to achieve the maximal benefit from this thirty-day program.

The goal is to connect with the specific emotional issues that may be inhibiting your healing. If you're reading this introduction, you're probably familiar with one or more of the excellent books on the mindbody connection that have been written over the past thirty years. You may have read one of Dr. John Sarno's books on back pain. You may be aware of Dr. Bernie Siegel's books on exceptional cancer patients. You may have heard of Norman Cousins' self-description of healing through laughter. You may be familiar with Simonton's work on positive imagery and the immune system. You may have seen Andrew Weil interviewed on television or read one of his books describing "Complementary Medicine."

These books are compelling, and the medical research is increasingly reinforcing that the mental and emotional aspects of illness can no longer be ignored or minimized in the practice of medicine. In my twenty-five years in medical training and practice, I can attest to the powerful effect of utilizing the mindbody connection to heal patients, and even myself (see the Foreword). Even if your pain or illness originated with a physical or structural condition, if it persists despite appropriate treatment, the mental and emotional aspects may be significant in making your symptoms worse, and therefore this workbook is useful in these cases, as well.

While more people are interested and more practitioners intrigued by the possibilities inherent in a mindbody approach to illness, the question remains how to integrate this into medical treatment. Understanding the mindbody connection is critical, and the books described above, and many others, do an excellent job of explaining and describing the research and clinical support for this relationship. However, my patients often find them insufficient in helping them to develop a practical treatment approach. Patients may be told to "think positively," "do relaxation exercises," "meditate," or "become mindful." But exactly how to do this is often unclear.

This Workbook may be used independently or in combination with the medical treatment program developed by your treating doctor. I hope that many primary care and specialty physicians who treat chronic pain, chronic fatigue, anxiety, irritable bowel syndrome, TMJ, etc. will see fit to recommend this book to their patients. Psychologists can utilize it as an adjunct to therapy, either individual, or group therapy. The Workbook can stimulate emotional connections that can be elaborated upon in therapy sessions.

It is the act of answering these questions and writing and making connections that is crucial to recovery, in my experience. Some may choose to type their answers on a computer, although freehand writing may have some advantages in terms of accessing the brain in a different way than typing does. Recording answers on a recording device (e.g. phone) can also be effective. If you write some particularly nasty stuff and are concerned someone may find the workbook, it is permissible to tear it up and throw that page away. Sometimes this can be therapeutic in and of itself. (The write and rip up approach is sometimes called "negative writing.")

# My Background

My first exposure to mindbody medicine was the diagnosis of Tension Myositis Syndrome (or TMS) which I received as a medical student at New York University in 1981. I had been suffering from severe knee pain, worse with running and basketball, for some time. During my freshman year in medical school, the knee pain became severe enough that I was forced to curtail these two recreational activities. When I did so, my knee pain got a little better, but any attempt to return to sports made it worse again.

I sought treatment at student health and was referred to an Orthopedic Professor, one of the New York Yankees' team physicians. He prescribed anti-inflammatory medication and an exercise program. I diligently performed these exercises and strengthened the muscles around my knees. Despite this added strength, I still had pain with any significant athletic activity.

The next step was the arthrogram, an x-ray test that involves the injection of a dye-containing solution into the knee joint. Yes, this was as painful as it sounds; especially when performed by a resident in radiology learning the procedure on my knees while his professor supervised him. The results were negative for any tear that would require surgery. They showed a "normal variant" appearance to my meniscal cartilage, which the orthopedic professor felt was not significant. I was advised to keep doing my exercises and that surgery was not likely to be helpful in my case.

My diagnosis remained tendinitis, "runner's knee." I sought out the advice of John E. Sarno, M.D., Professor of Rehabilitation Medicine at NYU. He had lectured to my class in anatomy during our first semester in school on the musculoskeletal system. He seemed a logical choice for recommendations about exercise or other rehabilitative techniques to help my knee recover.

The advice Dr. Sarno gave me when I entered his office was surprising and career modifying for me. After a very brief discussion of my symptoms and normal test results, he told me that, in his experience, 95% of these chronic pain syndromes were "tension related." Stunned at this unexpected twist, I responded that I had heard of migraine headaches being due to stress, but knee pain from basketball? His response was to invite me to his evening lecture on this subject that he gave to his patients. I could come in for a more detailed consultation after that seminar if I liked.

I attended the presentation with more than a little skepticism, but with a lot of interest. I had gradually become aware of the fact that I was prone to physical ailments related to stress. I had had some irritable bowel symptoms during my teenage years and I associated them with social events to which I was invited. Athletic competitions during college tended to provoke the same kinds of symptoms. My family doctor as a teenager had mentioned stress in response to a couple of my minor illnesses, but I wasn't yet sure that he was right.

The evening lecture was attended by about twenty or thirty individuals, all older than my 21 years, some considerably so. They seemed like a group of normal, well-adjusted people. The lecture began with a discussion of anatomy and worked its way through psychology and a description of the Tension Myositis Syndrome, as Dr. Sarno called it. Most of the discussion focused on back pain, but he mentioned that it was applicable to other painful conditions and a variety of "psychosomatic disorders." Specifically, he mentioned irritable bowel syndrome, allergies, asthma, and migraines.

Gradually, the explanations began not only to make sense to me, but explained to me a lot about myself. I noticed my own tendency to worry about my knee pain in the case examples given. I had been reading everything I could find in the medical school library about knee pain and was focused a lot on its cause and cure. My emphasis on structural variations in my legs (tibial torsion, or curved shin bone) or flat feet, led to no pain relief, but more worry. I had tried knee braces and arch supports without any change. Also, my past history of tension-related bowel symptoms and prior back spasms in college seemed eerily consistent with the profile of the TMS sufferer that Dr. Sarno described.

The clarity of this explanation for my knee pain, and other conditions, really struck a chord. As I walked home that evening I felt less worried and more hopeful than I had in quite a while. By the time I arrived home, I was both excited and yet very calm. I sat on the edge of my bed and thought about the evening. I could actually feel my tension level dropping and my knee pain disappearing. Over the next days and weeks, my knee pain resolved, and I did see Dr. Sarno in consultation and have an examination confirming that I possessed the characteristic "tender points" on examination of my back and buttocks.

I returned to active basketball and running. I occasionally had mild knee discomfort, but nothing like before and it didn't stop me from being active in sports. The beneficial effect of return to these loved pastimes and the stress release from these physical outlets only seemed to create more relaxation and well being. The negativity and worry about my knee had dissipated. Now, as a born worrier, I could go back to worrying about medical school, my social life, etc.

This last sentence is a truth of this work that Dr. Sarno elaborates in his writing. The pain was a distraction for me from dealing with other issues. It also became a hindrance in coping with these issues. I quickly became a believer and even a proselytizer to the cause of psycho-somatic medicine. Often this was not well received in a traditional medical school environment, both among my fellow students and faculty.

The following summer, with the help of a work-study grant, I performed 177 telephonic interviews under Dr. Sarno's auspices, and the results confirmed the validity of his approach with a large group of former patients. The details of this study are described in his books, including **Mind Over Back Pain** (MBP, see Bibliography). For me, they provided supporting evidence for my own experience with TMS and a basis for further understanding and treating the disorder.

Since that time, I have completed my medical education and residency training and been involved in clinical practice, academic work, and medical quality research and review. I always maintained a TMS outlook and approach to treating chronic back pain and other conditions. Not infrequently, I diagnosed patients as suffering from mindbody disorders including individuals with headaches, pelvic pain, and even eczema. Many of these patients benefited tremendously from learning about and applying the mindbody connection to their problem. However, I lacked a formal program or critical mass of patients to focus on treating mindbody disorders. Around 1995, after establishing a part-time private practice in Beverly Hills, California, I was fortunate enough to begin to receive referrals from Dr. Sarno's office in New York. These were individuals who lived on the West Coast and had familiarity with TMS from his books or friends who were his patients.

As I began to see more people who were interested and informed about this disorder and motivated to use a mindbody approach, I was able to improve my ability to treat these conditions. I began to offer a monthly seminar inspired by Dr. Sarno's educational lectures to his patients. I made an audio recording of the seminar for people who were unable to attend the presentation. Over time I developed a second audio recording on diagnosis and treatment of TMS and its implications. A third recording (eventually digitally remastered) evolved out of the relationship I developed with a psychotherapist in Los Angeles, himself a successful TMS patient. Most of the patients presented to my office with back or neck pain, but there were also patients with iliotibial band syndrome (thigh pain), arm pain, RSI, temporo-mandibular joint syndrome (TMJ), headaches, and irritable bowel syndrome. Again and again, I found that educating people about the mindbody connection and teaching them to think psycho-logically was crucial to their improvement.

My decision to write this MindBody Workbook is based upon the need that many of these patients have described to me for a disciplined, structured approach to working through their pain problem. There are not an insignificant number who get the "eureka, I've found it" response to being exposed to TMS theory or treatment, as I did in 1981. Some of these get better from reading one of Dr. Sarno's books (or my book) and never seek formal medical consultation. Nonetheless, many do require a period of self-examination and "re-programming" of the vicious cycle of worry, fear, anger, and pain that I allude to in my own case. I have regularly advised patients to keep a journal about the topics covered in this Workbook and find this practice extremely valuable. The questions in this book have developed from my experience with mindbody disorders and the ideas of the workers in this field that have come before me. (see Bibliography)

As always, I recommend a formal medical examination prior to utilizing this workbook. I address the issue of which doctors may be helpful to you in Appendix Two. I recommend that you seek out a primary care physician or appropriate subspecialist in your area. Have an appropriate workup to exclude serious or life-threatening causes of back and neck pain such as tumors, fractures, cancer, or infection. If the doctor supports a "conservative," i.e. non-surgical approach to your problem, even if that doctor is not familiar with mindbody approaches or TMS, you can consider using this Workbook as part of your treatment program.

It is my hope that in the not-too-distant future that this Workbook and its equivalents, will be routinely recommended by many practitioners of different medical and alternative specialties for their patients with chronic pain, mindbody, and stress-related disorders. The recognition and acknowledgment of mindbody disorders in the medical field would alleviate a great deal of suffering. In the meantime, this Workbook, the bibliography, and other materials, some described on my web site **www.mindbodymedicine.com**, are available for the actively exploring individual seeking a MindBody approach to healing their condition.

# Psychosomatic and MindBody Disorders

In this Workbook I use the term "psychosomatic disorder" (from the Greek roots 'psycho' or spirit, mind and 'soma' or body) to refer to medical conditions that are caused or made worse by emotional distress, tension, or stress. A distinction has typically been made between these conditions and purely "physical" or "structural" conditions. While a broken leg would clearly fall into the latter category, non-traumatic illness does not easily lend itself to these distinctions. For example, a cold or upper respiratory infection is an illness "caused" by a virus. But we know that people under emotional stress have physical evidence of impaired immune response and may be more prone to "catching" a cold. So this too, is a "psychosomatic" disorder.

The term psychosomatic disorder has acquired a bad reputation because of being inaccurately associated with "faking" an illness. Many patients and even doctors make this mistake in usage. In addition, it is incorrectly associated with the "hypochondriac" who is represented in the media as a neurotic, unhappy person constantly worried about his body. Anyone can get a psychosomatic disorder. Although certain personality characteristics may predispose to experiencing emotions in physical symptoms, these characteristics are anything but those of a neurotic loser. Many high achieving, responsible, successful, perfectionists suffer from back pain, migraine headaches, and the like.

In a broader sense, all conditions are mindbody or psychosomatic. While fracturing your leg may be somatic in nature, an individual's response to being in a cast, using crutches, and dealing with disability certainly has a huge emotional component. Physicians tend to incorporate this part of healing in a nonverbal or implicit way. An encouraging remark, a reassuring touch, and good listening goes a long way to help a patient to heal.

What our "modern" approach to psychosomatic medicine offers in addition to reassurance is an explicit use of the mindbody connection as a therapeutic tool. This Workbook offers you the opportunity to tap into powerful healing forces previously described by such derogatory terms as the "placebo" response and make them work for you. By answering the questions openly and in an uncensored fashion, you have the opportunity to access the unconscious mind's reservoir of memory, emotion, and knowledge and use it for your benefit.

Self-awareness and utilization of the mindbody connection can actually cure some of the conditions that you suffer from. My work with back pain has demonstrated this to me and to many successful patients. For conditions such as asthma and rheumatoid arthritis, the goal is fewer symptoms and flare-ups. For patients with cancer, less pain, a stronger immune system, and longer remissions may be possible with a mindbody program.

The medical community is still somewhat hostile or indifferent to these ideas, although I believe this is changing. Psychosomatic or mindbody medicine is something that many physicians are uncomfortable with because of their scientific training in a reductionistic approach to disease that looks for the abnormal molecule that causes the illness. Subspecialty medicine has perpetuated the fractionation of the human body into different segments that are treated by different practitioners. In addition, many physicians lack psychological self-awareness. Persons who succeed in pre-medical training often have a narrow worldview that allows the dedication to school and career that is rewarded in the medical admissions process. Finally, a lack of training and a lack of role models during medical school and residency hamper those who would like to incorporate a more holistic view of disease.

George Engel, M.D. (see bibliography) wrote eloquently about medicine's mind/body split and failure to take a biopsychosocial perspective on illness. He spoke about "exploring the requirements of a medical model that would account for the reality of diabetes and schizophrenia as human experiences as well as disease abstraction..." Psychosomatic approaches incorporate this broader view of health and disease into diagnosis and treatment.

# Supportive Research

An interesting and important article was recently published in the Journal of the American Medical Association (JAMA) by Joshua Smyth, PhD and his colleagues at the State University of New York (SUNY) Stony Brook School of Medicine (JAMA 4/14/99, volume 281 no. 14, p. 1304-09). It speaks to the effectiveness of a writing program for patients with physical illness. The researchers studied individuals with asthma and others with rheumatoid arthritis. Participants in the study were asked to write for twenty minutes on three consecutive days a week. Those in the experimental group were told to write about the most stressful experience they had ever undergone. The control group was told to write about their plans for the day. Participants were asked to write continuously, without regard for spelling or stylistic concerns. Over the course of the study and the four-month follow-up period, individuals who wrote about emotional issues showed significant clinical improvements in objective measurements of their disease. The asthma patients responded within two weeks and change for those with rheumatoid arthritis took a few weeks longer.

This study shows the potential power of expressing one's thoughts and feelings in writing. This MindBody Workbook has the potential to accomplish much more as it is designed to specifically focus on issues that I have found to be pertinent to treating psychosomatic disorders. Individuals are given a great deal more guidance in what to write and how to express themselves. This should enhance the emotional benefit, reduce boredom, and gradually teach a more emotionally aware approach to living. The self-growth inherent in this process offers the reader the opportunity to obtain more self-insight and hence further improvement over time. Once completed, the user can come back to this Workbook and re-read and re-use it over time.

Diane Berry and James Pennebaker of Southern Methodist University published another article that addresses the issue of verbal expression of emotion and its impact on health in 1993. (Psychotherapeutics and Psychosomatics 1993: 59: 11-19) They reviewed findings of other research studies that demonstrate that verbal and nonverbal expression of emotion is related to immediate reductions in autonomic nervous system activity. They concluded that the verbal expression of traumatic experiences by writing or talking improves physical health, enhances immune function and is associated with fewer medical visits.

Of note, Dr. Sarno (**Healing Back Pain** (HBP)) has hypothesized the level of autonomic nervous system activity to be crucial in the TMS pain process. In addition, autonomic nervous system hyperactivity has also been associated with high blood pressure, anxiety, and other conditions. Thus the finding that verbal expression of emotion can lower this level of activity lends further support to the goals of this Workbook. The article also speaks to non-verbal expression of emotion and notes that less research is available regarding this factor.

Several researchers from the University of Miami published a study in 1993 that looked at healthy undergraduates who were positive for Epstein-Barr virus (EBV). These individuals were divided into two study groups. The first group was assigned to write or talk about stressful events during three weekly twenty-minute sessions. The other group was told to write about trivial events. The individuals assigned to the group that wrote about stressful events had significantly lower EBV antibody titers than the group that wrote about trivial events. (Journal of Consulting and Clinical Psychology, 1994, vol 62, no. 1, 130-140.) This suggests better immune system control over the virus, which can remain dormant in many individuals without symptoms. The group that spoke about their stress did even better than the group that wrote about emotions.

This study again speaks to the value of expressing our emotions in a regular, programmatic way. While speaking into a recorder was more effective than writing, the study supports both approaches as effective in altering immune system responses. I would not object to individuals who would prefer to complete their Workbook by speaking into a recorder. I have found, however, that for most people, writing works well, is easier to do, offers a better opportunity to concentrate, and most importantly, is easier to review and as portable.

Emotional issues are crucial in a variety of disorders that are typically treated primarily as "physical conditions." A recent study conducted at the Mind/Body Center for Women's Health at Beth Israel Deaconess Medical Center in Boston (described in the Mind/Body Newsletter vol. VII, No. 2, 1998, p.7) looked at depression and infertility. Within six months of completing a ten-week group stress program, 44% of 174 women who had prior difficulty conceiving had become pregnant. Women who were the least depressed had a 24% pregnancy rate and those who were most depressed had a 60% pregnancy rate.

The reason that the more depressed patients got pregnant at a higher rate is because the intervention (group stress program) helped those who were depressed. Depression might interfere with hormones that affect ovulation and implantation of embryos. Women who could not get pregnant for other structural reasons (scarring or adhesions, for example) were not helped by the program. This study presents more evidence that emotional factors should be considered in a wide variety of medical conditions. An organized treatment program with specialists in the field is ideal. This Workbook can be an adjunct to such treatment.

More scientific evidence is presented in Chapter VI of my book *Think Away Your Pain* for this treatment approach.

Note that while this Workbook was originally developed in 1999, it has been used with patients and readers up until the present when it is being reformatted for print on demand in 2022. The value is still in the writing; the prompts make the journaling easier, and the process is the goal. Write, think, learn more about yourself, and you make connections and good things happen from this.

# Thirty Day Program

Why, you might ask, a thirty-day program for pain relief? I have found that many individuals suffering from mindbody disorders can make dramatic progress within the first thirty days after the diagnosis is made. To accomplish this, individuals need to learn how to "listen" for the mindbody connection in their life. The approach that I have found works the best is to make a daily, concerted effort to accept and understand the diagnosis. I have found that keeping a daily journal can be an important component of the education, introspection, and self-awareness required to heal the disorder. This includes such conditions as fibromyalgia, TMS, tension headaches, irritable bowel syndrome, RSI, temporo-mandibular joint pain or TMJ.

Some people notice significant pain relief within days. However, this is not a cure, by any means. The immediate relief of pain may be due to a reduction in worry about the pain, even due to a placebo response to a new therapy. But a long-lasting response is what we desire in treating these conditions. This requires working through more issues, learning how to apply these principles during stressful days and easy ones, and learning to relate to others as a healthier individual.

TMS and other mindbody disorders may serve as a distraction (see Chapter 2, MBP) from unpleasant emotions including anger, fear and unresolved grief. This serves a real function for the unconscious mind, even as it causes us to suffer from real physical pain. Patients, including those who are most successful in initially responding to the diagnosis/treatment, often go through doubting periods. It is my contention that this doubt is inherent to the condition. The doubt is a manifestation of the unconscious mind's desire to return to the method of distraction that it has utilized to avoid the unpleasant emotional issues. Learning to deal with and overcome the doubt is an important part of a long-lasting cure and an integral part of this workbook.

You might ask, "after thirty days, if I'm not cured, what do I do?" There will be a more detailed discussion of this subject at the end of this book. Briefly, if you're much better, but not totally pain-free, continue or repeat the Workbook cycle for another thirty days. Two months is a relatively short period of time for individuals who have often struggled with these conditions for years. Furthermore, it is a LOT LESS expensive than going to endless physical treatments for the pain that often provides temporary relief. For individuals not making significant progress, a revisit with your doctor is appropriate to reassess and reaffirm the diagnosis and treatment. If you are seeing a mindbody practitioner, this is a typical timepoint at which adjunctive psychotherapy may be recommended at a revisit or telephone follow-up.

Plan on setting aside between ten and twenty minutes a day to use this workbook during the thirty days of this program, perhaps somewhat more time during the first week. Avoid skipping more than one day a week or spending more than ninety minutes a day. Either can lead to a lack of success. The overuse of these materials, paradoxically, can lead to more worry and a renewed fear-tension cycle, rather the reverse. The goal of all this work is to enable you to live your live more freely and to empower you to heal. Fifteen to forty minutes a day (including the Workbook and other reading on TMS and the mindbody connection) is achievable for most people and enough time to learn and apply these concepts.

Crucial to success using this workbook is the willingness on the part of the user to notice their feelings and record and try to understand them. Try not to censor your feelings, be explicit and allow them to flow. Sit with your feelings, attempt to reflect and probe deeper. While this is not easy for most of us to do, it is important to try, in order to break the troubling pattern of feelings being experienced as pain, rather than emotion. When needed, use the additional blank pages at the end of the workbook, or obtain a blank notebook to record your thoughts and feelings. Maintaining a journal can also be continued, after the completion of this program, on a regular, if not daily basis using a blank notebook.

Not every question will be relevant to each individual or each disorder that can benefit from working with the mindbody connection. Respond to the questions and issues that are relevant to you and you'll learn what you need to learn: how to acknowledge emotion and connect it with your physical symptoms. In the process of doing this, you are likely to begin feeling better physically and emotionally. Be patient, this takes time.

It is normal for emotions to be stirred up while using the Workbook. Breaking patterns and developing insight inevitability involves looking at our lives and ourselves in a different way than we typically do. Making connections with old feelings can bring up the grief of an old loss that has been submerged or the elation of a forgotten dream or goal that we've ignored for too long. If for any reason the emotionality becomes too intense, this is a good reason to consider a course of psychotherapy or counseling. A relationship with a caring professional can help guide us back to safe shores, this time with the insight that we lacked when we didn't face these intense experiences directly.

# Day Zero

**Date** / 8 /2023

The program begins when the diagnosis is made or when you make a commitment to include emotional healing in your treatment. The day that you see your physician is when the diagnosis is typically confirmed. You may suspect your condition has a mindbody component, you may have even made some progress with reading one of the books mentioned in the bibliography. But the benefit of seeing a doctor with a mindbody orientation is substantial. There is nothing that can truly replace that face-to-face interview with someone sensitive to these issues. Similarly, the physical examination should reassure you that you have the diagnostic findings such as tender points and no other significant neurological findings. A review with this doctor of your x-rays and MRI scans (or reports of same), or other test results can reassure you that there is nothing alarming in the structural area that accounts for your symptoms.

In the event that you see a doctor to exclude other conditions, but not one who is comfortable making a psychosomatic diagnosis or initiating a mindbody treatment plan, a slightly different mindset is necessary. Day Zero for you is the day you bring up with your doctor the idea that you believe some/all of your condition is tension related. Or it may be the day that you leave your doctor's office with the recommendation to pursue a conservative program (for back pain, typically a prescription for physical therapy or home exercise and anti-inflammatory or pain medication) and decide to incorporate this Workbook into that conservative recommendation from your doctor. While this is not ideal, the reality is that there are still relatively few physicians comfortable with a medical diagnosis of a psychosomatic disorder (such as TMS, irritable bowel syndrome, tension headaches) and even fewer with experience in its treatment.

Goals for Day Zero are to become clear about why the diagnosis/approach applies to you. For this purpose, grab the pen that will be your companion for the next thirty days of this program, and answer the following questions:

**1) Why do you feel a mindbody approach makes sense in relation to your problem?**

*Because my symptoms have been on-going and travel throughout my body, appearing suddenly and then many times disappearing just as suddenly. Also, I can have multiple symptoms happening simultaneously with many having either an unexplainable or routine explanation.*

**2) What aspects of your personality (see checklist) might predispose you to Tension Myositis Syndrome (TMS) and/or other psychosomatic disorders? How does these ways of dealing with life generate a lot of tension/stress for you?**

   ✓    perfectionism
   ✓    self-critical
   ✓    overly responsible
   ✓    control-oriented
   ✓    people-pleaser
   ✓    highly conscientious

*I have to be overly responsible. I'm all that I have. I beat myself up for all of the past bad decisions I've made, and the lasting impact on me. I have to please people, because if I don't, I'll either lose them (my job, my sister) and I don't want that.*

2

**3) Have you suffered from other medical conditions on the list below?** (Some or all of these may be caused or made worse by a similar mindbody connection? (check off the following))

_yes - many, multiple and some simultaneously. When one leaves, another starts. There is rarely a period when I can remember where nothing wasn't happening_

| | |
|---|---|
| ✓ | allergies |
| ✓ | asthma |
| ✓ | fibromylagia |
| ✓ | irritable bowel syndrome |
| ✓ | temporomandibular joint syndrome (TMJ) |
| | unexplained pelvic pain |
| | tension headaches |
| ✓ | TMS _(Back?)_ |
| | migraine headaches |
| ✓ | (other_____specify) _Rashes, sinusitis, reactions to bites, GI disorders (Reflux), shingles_ |

**4) Did your doctor's examination provide any clues that assisted her in confirming a mindbody diagnosis and excluding structural issues? If so what?**

_Only one - Dr Perkins - who said I couldn't get my stomach calmed until I got my head calmed. Otherwise all of the research I've done is on my own._
_Oh, and a PT in Century City suggested it as well as a pain management doctor._

**5)** **What x-ray changes or laboratory findings were you informed of regarding your condition? Are any of these inconsistent, inconclusive, or benign? Do they support a mindbody diagnosis or exclude serious pathology in your case?** (if this is not relevant, ask yourself...how has being informed of your test results alarmed you?)

By & large, most results since TMS started have been unremarkable. I did have Gallstone + an E. Coli diagnosis (which had it arrived sooner could have prevented an appendectomy) Most are inflammation related, and the results are (thank GOD) unremarkable.

**6)** **On a scale of 1-10 (ten being most certain), how comfortable are you with the diagnosis of a mindbody or psychosomatic disorder? How comfortable are you with using an emotional healing approach to getting well?** (Why...what is impeding your getting to a ten?)

| uncomfortable | 1 | 2 | 3 | 4 | 5 | 6 | 7 | 8 | 9 | 10 | comfortable |
|---|---|---|---|---|---|---|---|---|---|---|---|

VERY COMFORTABLE — I am utterly exasperated and cannot continue living like this. The constant symptoms + chronic worry have essentially stopped my life. Its interfered with work, tempered any joy, made me afraid to go out, or doesn't allow me to relax in any way!

# Week One

The goals of this week are to solidify your understanding of the material that you have already been exposed to about your diagnosis and the mindbody connection. Your goal for this week is to read, or re-read, one of the books that pertains to your condition, in its entirety. For back pain sufferers, I recommend Dr. Sarno's **Healing Back Pain**. I find that reading a chapter a day of the one of the books (see Bibliography) reinforces the reality of the mindbody connection in your condition and motivates you to complete this workbook. My 2014 book, **Think Away Your Pain,** is a work that focuses on chronic pain of mindbody origin, emphasizing treatment and the power to the brain to transform.

Systematic re-reading of the material offers an opportunity for deeper understanding of the condition and begins the process of "reprogramming" your nervous system to heal. It takes repetition to create a habit or develop a skill (think of playing the piano). Similarly, it takes weeks (or months) of study and self-understanding to break the pattern of expressing emotions in physical symptoms. Hence the rereading of these books and the, at times, repetitive nature of the questions to follow in this Workbook. It takes times for emotional connections to catch up with our more rapid intellectual understanding

When you read a chapter, focus on how the concepts apply to you personally. It's not enough to just have a general understanding of the theory. It's crucial to reflect on the similarities to your own symptoms and personality and delve deeper. You will be asked each day to think about and write about your feelings and emotions from the current or prior day. Try to express yourself spontaneously and unchecked. Read and reflect on what you've written at the end of each session, and more thoroughly at the end of each week. Even if your problem is tension headaches, irritable bowel syndrome, or TMJ, rather than the one described in a particular book, these books can be helpful to you if you try to apply the concepts to yourself.

# Day One

**Date** ___1___ / ___9___ / ___23___

Today is the day after the diagnosis (or other psychosomatic condition) was made and you've now begun the education and self-exploration phase in earnest.

1) **What went on in your life today?** (The focus here is emotionally, not "went to the movies". "I got upset at … and think that the reason is …" is the content we are looking for. If the day has been psychologically uninteresting, then look back at the last week and write about your feelings.) Again, don't censor yourself, let it flow…

I felt that my team was undervalued by Paul. I feel like I'm not respected and that the "jury is still out on me". I felt embarrassed that Nordstrom gave me a flat out no on the show because the brand is not luxury enough. Like what the fuck did I do?

2) **What connection between these emotions and your symptoms did you notice today?** (It's all right if you don't notice one right away. The key thing is thinking about the connection. The pain may often lessen or disappear before you identify any specific emotion.)

My stomach which felt ok yesterday started to blow up today – especially after Dr. S called me. The reflux symptoms got worse.

**3) In your reading and the reflecting about your condition you did today, describe how the ideas resonated and reminded you of YOURSELF.** (An ongoing theme with people who successfully heal their pain is an ability to connect to the stories of other successful patients or case examples from one of the books. The ability to see yourself in these examples makes the diagnosis much more real.)

It really didn't. I only remember past experiences where thats happened. When a doctor (Dr. Piken) said "no" on further evaluation, and the symptoms suddenly stopped.

**4) What concerns, questions, or doubts remain for you about the diagnosis of a psychosomatic disorder (or a mindbody approach to healing?** (Save these sections for your next doctor visit if they are not resolved or answered by your further study)

I know that I have a psychosomatic disorder. I'm not in denial! I may have some legitimate heartburn or other issues, but I know that my stressors aggravate them. I don't know how to quell the stressors + how they affect me, if I'm so used to the stress that it doesn't seem unusuall. Its just standard for me now — Is excercise (or lack thereof) a component?

**5) What physical activities have you done today?** (e.g. walking, exercise, etc.) Returning to physical activity is an important part of a mindbody treatment program. I caution people not to overdo it during their first few weeks. Many individuals are quite deconditioned from overprotecting their body and avoiding pain. Also, I find that any flare-up of pain can increase the doubt issue and prefer to gradually have the patient increase activity while they are becoming more secure in their acceptance and belief in the diagnosis.

_None! Sitting at my b'ing desk and barely getting up to eat or go to the bathroom. That's a problem!_

# Day Two

**Date** _____/_____/_____

1) **What happened in your life today?** (Identify and describe your emotional reactions to events, work, and relationships. What do you feel may be the deeper cause of these reactions or feelings?)

_____

_____

_____

_____

_____

2) **Were your symptoms better or worse than usual?** (Relate this to your emotional state)

_____

_____

_____

_____

_____

**3) Describe how you see yourself reflected in your reading today.** (What ideas did this give you for your own treatment?)

_____

_____

_____

_____

_____

_____

**4) Have you had any time for yourself today...what did you think about?** (Start planning a few minutes to yourself each day, preferably out of the car...where you can just walk and/or sit and relax).

_____

_____

_____

_____

_____

# Day Three

**Date** _____ / _____ / _____

1) **What happened in your life today?** (Describe emotional reactions to events and relationships...feel free to spend five minutes on this, or fifteen, depending on how well you are able to access feelings today. Don't rush this work. It's okay to sit and stare at the page for a few minutes or daydream. Daydreaming can be part of healing. Getting in touch with emotions takes time and often a suitable place—a quiet, unrushed interval.)

_____

_____

_____

_____

_____

2) **If your pain was better today, are you giving yourself some credit for it?** (Self-critical patients often downplay their improvement and often continue to worry about a relapse). What else have you given yourself credit for today? (or this week...)

_____

_____

_____

_____

_____

3) **What did you do for fun today**? (This can be as simple as playing a CD you like in the car or singing in the shower. Beginning to relax leads to release of tension and symptoms.) **What do you like to do for fun? What will you do tomorrow that you truly enjoy?**

_____

_____

_____

_____

_____

4) **Physically, have you exerted yourself today or been a little more active? What did you do and for about how long or how far?** (Note key word here is about. I don't want you to time your walks to the second or count the stairs you walk. That's perfectionism. Although the treatment is not to change your personality (even if you could), learning to tone down is helpful. Approximate is in this case (and many others) quite good enough. )

_____

_____

_____

_____

# Day Four

**Date** _____/_____/_____

**1) What went on in your life today?**

_____

_____

_____

_____

_____

**2) Today make a list of anything you think may be stressing you.** (Just a list, no editing or commentary, yet.)

1) _____

2) _____

3) _____

4) _____

5) _____

6) _____

7) _____

8) _____

9) _____

10) _____

**Now place a checkmark above beside any item that you can influence or potentially change. Place an "x" next to anything that is not modifiable or controllable.** Recopy the x list on a piece of scrap paper, look at each item…and then toss it away. These are things you need to let go of. Make a separate list below of the checkmarked items starting with the most important at the top.

_____

_____

_____

_____

_____

Which item can you start working on today or tomorrow? Write this down here _____ _____and then elaborate on what you will do to act upon it. Then act! The other items may be suitable for a later time.)

3) **Feel like a walk- or run-in place and a stretch now? Do it!** (Letting go of control is a big challenge for some individuals…)

_____

_____

_____

_____

_____

# Day Five

**Date** _____/_____/_____

**1) What is going on in your life today?** (Comment also on the issue you decided to focus on in yesterday's exercise)

_____

_____

_____

_____

_____

**2) How did today's reading impact you or remind you of yourself?**

_____

_____

_____

_____

_____

_____

**3) Think about your "self-talk" today. What messages do you give yourself that reinforce a pain-tension cycle?** (Sit and think about this for a while— How is your reaction to twinges, sensations, and pain making it harder for the muscles to relax? Do you worry about a structural cause or getting worse?)

_____

_____

_____

_____

_____

_____

**4) What are you most afraid of in your life?** (We will come back to this later…just start writing here. Take some time if needed)

_____

_____

_____

_____

_____

_____

# Day Six

**Date** _____/_____/_____

1) **What's going in your life today—focus on relationships.** (At whom are you most angry at the present time…take some time to elaborate on your feelings and legitimate them to yourself. At the same time, identify and elaborate on the feelings and any connection you see to your pain.)

_____

_____

_____

_____

_____

_____

2) **How does today's reading (bibliography) help you to understand your problem?**

_____

_____

_____

_____

_____

_____

3) **What has been the reaction from friends and relatives you've told about your diagnosis? How do you feel about their reaction?** (One issue that I deal with in mindbody treatment is the varied and challenging responses from friends. Some people are supportive, but many are skeptical, mocking, or critical of a "psychological" treatment for back pain and other conditions. Learning to deal with this is part of resuming your life and getting healthy.)

_____

_____

_____

_____

_____

4) **Are you getting more active physically?** (Why/why not? What are you feeling about your bodily movements and postures? Try to describe your feelings about your body and you're hopefully improving sense of fluidity in movement. I often find that as patient's fear of pain decreases, the comfort of movement improves dramatically.)

_____

_____

_____

_____

_____

# Day Seven

**Date** _____/_____/_____

1) **How do you feel today emotionally?** (What's making you anxious or upset today or lately? Be as detailed as possible as the feelings and what you believe may be underlying them)

_____

_____

_____

_____

2) **In your reading today, what additional insights has the material led you to about your condition and accepting this diagnosis/approach for yourself?** (Belief in the mindbody connection is clearly a critical element in getting well.)

_____

_____

_____

_____

_____

**3) What is/was your family's way of dealing with anger?** (Expressive, repressive, somatic, or substance use— How has your way of dealing with this emotion been affected by your family and how could this be contributing to your stress?)

_____

_____

_____

_____

_____

_____

**4) What physical activities do you look forward to doing when you're pain free?** (List them— What feelings are evoked when you sit and think about doing these activities? visualize yourself doing one or two of these)

_____

_____

_____

_____

_____

_____

# Week Two

The first goal for the second week is to review the first week and solidify any outstanding issues concerning the subject material. Start by reviewing your first week's journal entries for any recurrent themes that reflect areas that you need to focus on emotionally. During this week, you will be asked to explore more deeply your long-standing emotional issues. Since I want to make this Workbook practical and possible to fit into your hectic life, I won't expect you to do outside reading this week, although you may choose to read or reread any of the books from the bibliography ALONG with completing the Workbook pages. The task of writing your answers in this Workbook need not take longer than 10-20 minutes a day. You need this time to decompress from the day and reflect and understand yourself and the mindbody connection.

## Day Eight (week one recap)

1) **Look through what you've written during the past week. What concepts keep coming up?** (Are certain emotions predominant, is doubt common, and are you hopeful or sad?) **Summarize your first week of working on this program and your goals for the next week physically and psychologically.**

_____

_____

_____

_____

**2) Has this program affected your activity level so far?** (Describe the positive changes? Have you had more pain-free intervals? (acknowledge and give yourself credit for them) Try to quantify the change (an estimate is fine here).)

_____

_____

_____

_____

_____

_____

**3) What else in your life has been positive this week?** (Take some time to reflect on why this makes you feel good)

_____

_____

_____

_____

_____

_____

# Day Nine

**Date** _____/_____/_____

1) **How do you feel today emotionally?** (What made you happy today? Or this week if you must—people with these conditions often have a hard time focusing on the positive. Elaborate on this...)

_____

_____

_____

_____

_____

2) **What about your work (substitute parenting, caretaking, or hobby if appropriate) gets you excited or stimulated?** (Describe the feelings and any connections you can make to your past?)

_____

_____

_____

_____

_____

**3) What about your work makes you the most angry and frustrated?**

_____

_____

_____

_____

_____

_____

**4) Overall, does the fulfillment of your work exceed the nuisances?** (Are there alternatives for you?)

_____

_____

_____

_____

_____

_____

# Day Ten

**Date** _____/_____/_____

1) **What's going on in your life?** (Anything else about work, for example)

_____

_____

_____

_____

_____

_____

2) **How are you dealing with issues differently?** (How would you like to be responding emotionally in a different fashion to stressful situations? Can you connect this to your pain level?)

_____

_____

_____

_____

_____

_____

**3) Is there a loss in your life that keeps coming back to you and feels like it's still fresh?** (Describe it in detail. Take time to reflect and write about this source of grief.)

_____

_____

_____

_____

_____

_____

**4) Physically, are there supportive or positioning devices (or physical treatments that provide only temporary relief) that are no longer necessary and are acting as a "crutch" or impediment to your healing?** (Are you ready to stop them? If you used these in the past and have stopped, reflect on how their use reinforced your concept of sickness.)

_____

_____

_____

_____

_____

_____

# Day Eleven

**Date** _____/_____/_____

1) **What's the most difficult situation that you faced today?** (in terms of stress or emotionally, of course)

_____

_____

_____

_____

_____

_____

2) **Looking back at other illnesses you've had, reflect on one or more that seems connected to stress or a specific event?** (Describe how it's connected, and why)

_____

_____

_____

_____

_____

**3) If you could go back to that period in your life, how would you deal with things differently emotionally?**

_____

_____

_____

_____

_____

_____

**4) Can you see how this change might have led to a different outcome?** (How does this thought make you feel? Patients often have to deal with guilt about wishing they had known more in the past about the mindbody connection. Be explicit about these feelings and forgive yourself. You did not have this awareness then.)

_____

_____

_____

_____

_____

_____

# Day Twelve

**Date** _____/_____/_____

**1) What is the issue that you've struggled with a loved one about recently?** (How are you feeling about this struggle?)

_____

_____

_____

_____

_____

_____

**2) Does this struggle remind you of any past conflicts in relationships? (elaborate)**

_____

_____

_____

_____

_____

_____

**3)  Any connection between these feelings and your pain?**

_____

_____

_____

_____

_____

_____

**4)  Have you learned from friends and family of examples of their own psychosomatic illnesses?** (What do these examples have to teach you about yours?)

_____

_____

_____

_____

_____

_____

5) **In the weeks you've been writing in this Workbook, have there been medical cases discussed in the media that have reinforced a mindbody approach or made you skeptical about it?** (Discuss your concerns and feelings? Also, these concerns may be appropriate to discuss at a follow-up visit with your doctor)

_____

_____

_____

_____

_____

_____

# Day Thirteen

**Date** _____/_____/_____

**1) What are you angry about this week?**

_____

_____

_____

_____

_____

**2) When was the angriest you've ever been?** (Who, what, where, and why?)

_____

_____

_____

_____

_____

_____

**3) When were you angry with your parents?**

_____

_____

_____

_____

_____

_____

_____

**4) How did they react to your being angry?**

_____

_____

_____

_____

_____

_____

**5)  Does this affect your likelihood to acknowledge your angry feelings?**

_____

_____

_____

_____

_____

_____

_____

# Day Fourteen

**Date** _____ / _____ / _____

1) **What issues today/this week did you take responsibility for and how did that make you feel?**

_____

_____

_____

_____

_____

_____

2) **Are you a responsible person?** (How so/not and why? What does this mean to you?)

_____

_____

_____

_____

_____

_____

**3) What pressures do you feel precisely because of taking responsibility? What are the frustrations of being responsible for you?** (Take time with this.)

_____

_____

_____

_____

_____

_____

**4) How can you take emotional breaks from being responsible (hours, minutes, weekends, etc.)?** (What would this mean to you?)

_____

_____

_____

_____

_____

# Week Three

This is a week to work on exploring emotional issues and hindrances in your life. Begin to explore getting more active and re-conditioned physically. Brisker walks and more activity may be suitable this week. Start to explore breaking patterns and habits into which you have fallen. Spend some time daily appreciating the good things in your life, including, I trust, the improvement in your symptoms.

### Day Fifteen (Week two recap)

**Date _____/_____/_____**

1) **Re-read your entries from last week. What seems to be most the one issue that re-curs in your writing and your mind?** (Learning to trust your instinct is really important.)

_____

_____

_____

_____

_____

_____

2) **Given this important issue, what would it take to overcome or deal with this more effectively?** (Can you start on that process...what steps do you take first?)

_____

_____

_____

_____

_____

_____

_____

3) **What activities are you planning for the next few months, as you feel better and better?** (How does this planning make you feel? It's natural to be worried, excited, and fearful about this.)

_____

_____

_____

_____

_____

_____

4) **In the weeks you've been writing in this Workbook have there been medical cases discussed in the media that have reinforced a mindbody approach or made you skeptical about it?** (Discuss your concerns and feelings? (Also, these concerns may be appropriate to discuss at a follow-up visit with your doctor))

_____

_____

_____

_____

_____

David Schechter, M.D.

# Day Sixteen

**Date** _____/_____/_____

**1) What's going on in your life emotionally?**

_____

_____

_____

_____

_____

**2) Looking back at the list of things you could/could not control from Day Four, is there another issue that you need to deal with?** (Write it here). (What are the emotional difficulties in facing this issue?)

_____

_____

_____

_____

_____

**3) Is there a reason that this issue (or others on the list) has been difficult for you to face?** (Elaborate on how this relates to your past experiences.)

_____

_____

_____

_____

_____

_____

_____

**4) What are you doing right lately?** (Give yourself credit)

_____

_____

_____

_____

_____

_____

_____

# Day Seventeen

**Date** _____/_____/_____

**1) Any feelings seem to predominate today?** (What specifically and why?)

_____

_____

_____

_____

_____

**2) Who or what tends to make you feel guilty?** (How do you respond to this guilt?)

_____

_____

_____

_____

_____

_____

_____

**3) Did your parents or other authority figures use guilt as a tool for motivation or manipulation?** (Describe what comes to mind in some detail.)

_____

_____

_____

_____

_____

_____

_____

**4) Does feeling guilty lead you to feel any other emotions such as sadness or anger?** (What is this like? Give an example if you can recall one.)

_____

_____

_____

_____

_____

_____

# Day Eighteen

**Date** _____/_____/_____

1) **How are you feeling today?** (Any guilty feelings?)

_____

_____

_____

_____

_____

_____

2) **How have your symptoms been of late?** (Have you been making a connection between pain and your feelings? How do they seem related?)

_____

_____

_____

_____

_____

_____

**3) What makes you feel anxious or trapped?**

_____

_____

_____

_____

_____

_____

_____

**4) Looking back, has this feeling been something you've dealt with before?** (Give an example of this. Describe what anxiety is like for you and how you deal with it now.)

_____

_____

_____

_____

_____

_____

# Day Nineteen

**Date** _____/_____/_____

**1) What's going on in your life?**

_____

_____

_____

_____

_____

**2) How have you been feeling about yourself lately? How is this different than usual?**

_____

_____

_____

_____

_____

3) **When you are excessively self-critical, what is it about?** (Specific issues, characteristics, or events)

_____

_____

_____

_____

_____

_____

4) **How could you moderate or modulate this self-criticism to be gentler to yourself?**

_____

_____

_____

_____

_____

_____

**5) When you think about your style of self-criticism, do you remind yourself of some-one?** (Who and why do you remind yourself of that person?)

---

---

---

---

---

---

# Day Twenty

**Date** _____/_____/_____

**1) What's going on in your life?**

_____

_____

_____

_____

_____

_____

**2) What's your biggest fear?** (Take some time to reflect on this)

_____

_____

_____

_____

_____

_____

**3) How much do you focus on this on a day-to-day basis?** (Why do you suspect that you focus on this so often?)

_____

_____

_____

_____

_____

_____

**4) Does this fear or any others inhibit you from doing something you want to do?** (What are you afraid of and why?)

_____

_____

_____

_____

_____

_____

**5) Do you avoid facing or dealing with this fear?** (How often and how?)

_____

_____

_____

_____

_____

# Day Twenty One

**Date** _____/_____/_____

1) **What stressed you today (or this week)?** (Describe the incident, your reaction, and why you think this made you react this way?)

_____

_____

_____

_____

_____

2) **What typically gets you feeling stressed most often?** (How does it happen and why?)

_____

_____

_____

_____

_____

_____

**3) When we say stressed about this reaction, are we really saying "angry", "afraid", "anxious" or something else?** (Try to pinpoint the feeling and what it means to you.)

_____

_____

_____

_____

_____

**4) What would have happened as a child if you felt this way?** (e.g. What would your parents have said or done?)

_____

_____

_____

_____

_____

_____

# Week Four

This is the week to start putting the work together. Start off again by rereading last week's entries in the Workbook. Sit and think...read slowly.

## Day Twenty Two

**Date** _____/_____/_____

1) **Which of the questions and answers seems to resonate with you most strongly?** (And why so?)

_____

_____

_____

_____

_____

_____

_____

**2) Try to find an example of this emotion in today's experience or perhaps a powerful one from the past that comes to mind.** (Describe your feelings and reaction)

_____

_____

_____

_____

_____

_____

_____

**3) Describe the connection between this and your pain.** (Have you noticed your pain subsiding or getting worse while you think or write about this emotion?)

_____

_____

_____

_____

_____

_____

**4) How have you been feeling about getting more physically active?** (What emotions come up when you start increasing your activity level?)

_____

_____

_____

_____

_____

_____

**5) What activities are planned for this week?** (Walks, dancing, swimming, etc.). (How does it feel to think about these pleasurable events?)

_____

_____

_____

_____

_____

_____

# Day Twenty Three

**Date** _____/_____/_____

1) **What's going on in your life today?**

_____

_____

_____

_____

_____

_____

2) **If you have pain, what do you do?** (Describe your feelings and reactions, as well as techniques.) (If you're pain-free, describe what you would do, if the pain returned)

_____

_____

_____

_____

_____

_____

**3)** **How does thinking about the pain make you feel?** (Is this different from a few weeks ago? How so?)

_____

_____

_____

_____

_____

_____

**4)** **What's your biggest fear about the pain?** (e.g. become disabled, surgery, pain medication, needles, loss of job)

_____

_____

_____

_____

_____

_____

**5) Is this fear something that worries you even without the pain?** (When and why?)

_____

_____

_____

_____

_____

_____

# Day Twenty Four

**Date** _____/_____/_____

**1) What are you most excited about in your life?**

_____

_____

_____

_____

_____

_____

**2) Do you take credit for this?** (Why or why not? Should you take more credit for your success?)

_____

_____

_____

_____

_____

_____

**3)  When you praise yourself, what is it typically for?** (e.g. being a good person, being smart, funny, good-looking) Why that characteristic?

_____  _____

_____  _____

_____  _____

_____  _____

_____  _____

**4)  What did your parents praise you for?** (How did that make you feel?)

_____  _____

_____  _____

_____  _____

_____  _____

_____  _____

**5) List some things you should praise yourself for...but rarely do.** (Why don't you?)

_____

_____

_____

_____

_____

_____

_____

# Day Twenty Five

**Date** _____/_____/_____

**1) What's going on in your life?**

_____

_____

_____

_____

_____

_____

**2) What activities make you feel centered and whole?** (Give an example of one and how you feel doing it?)

_____

_____

_____

_____

_____

_____

**3) Why aren't you doing this more often?**

_____

_____

_____

_____

_____

_____

_____

**4) What would you be doing for fifteen minutes a day that would make you feel more centered?** (What is the feeling of being centered like to you?)

_____

_____

_____

_____

_____

_____

**5) What physical activity have you done today—how did doing it make you feel?** (or the last time you did a physical activity it felt...)

_____

_____

_____

_____

_____

_____

# Day Twenty Six

**Date** _____ / _____ / _____

**1) What's going on in your life?**

_____

_____

_____

_____

_____

**2) Describe the last time you felt really angry and why?** (Be as vivid as you can recall.)

_____

_____

_____

_____

_____

_____

**3) Looking back, where did the anger come from inside of you?** (Have you felt exactly that way before? Describe this, as well.)

_____

_____

_____

_____

_____

_____

_____

**4) Do you find that you are able to acknowledge your anger when it happens?** (What does it feel like when it starts to develop? Does your anger become excessive? When?)

_____

_____

_____

_____

_____

# Day Twenty Seven

**Date** _____/_____/_____

**1) How are you feeling lately about your most important relationship?**

_____

_____

_____

_____

_____

**2) Anything been different in dealing with that person lately?** (How has that felt to you? Why?)

_____

_____

_____

_____

_____

_____

**3) What feelings are the most difficult for you to share with that person?** (Why is that? Are they the same feelings that you find hard to acknowledge to yourself?)

_____

_____

_____

_____

_____

_____

_____

**4) How has your pain been lately?** (Any insights into the connection between your emotions and your symptoms?)

_____

_____

_____

_____

_____

# Day Twenty Eight

**Date** _____/_____/_____

**1) What's going on with your work (office or home)?** (How are you feeling about this lately?)

_____

_____

_____

_____

_____

**2) What's the hardest thing about your work?** (How do you feel about that?)

_____

_____

_____

_____

_____

_____

_____

**3) How would you like your work to be different or your reaction to your work change?**
(Are either possible? How do you feel about this?)

_____

_____

_____

_____

_____

_____

**4) Refocus on what you enjoy about your work. What is this?** (How does it feel when work is going well?)

_____

_____

_____

_____

_____

_____

# Final Days

These final two days of the thirty-day cycle are a chance to summarize, reflect, and plan for the future. Start again by reviewing last week's entries. After reading them, take a little time to look over your complete entries, to date.

## Day Twenty Nine

Date _____/_____/_____

1) **Which seems most significant to you among your many entries in this workbook?** (Why?)

_____

_____

_____

_____

_____

_____

**2) What does your gut tell you about your condition?** (How is it connected to your feelings?)

_____

_____

_____

_____

_____

_____

**3) What do you need to do in the future to stay in touch with your emotions without the daily reminders from the workbook?** (Any ideas or feelings are fine here)

_____

_____

_____

_____

_____

_____

_____

**4) What do you need to work on to maintain your improvement and go even further with it?**

_____

_____

_____

_____

_____

_____

# Day Thirty

**Date** _____/_____/_____

1) **What's going on in your life?** (couldn't forget this question)

_____

_____

_____

_____

_____

_____

2) **When you doubt your diagnosis or the mindbody connection in your illness, what feelings come to mind?** (What are your fears or concerns?)

_____

_____

_____

_____

_____

_____

**3) What's the biggest thing you've learned about yourself during this month of writing in this workbook?** (How is that important to you?)

_____

_____

_____

_____

_____

_____

**4) What would you like to do differently in the future?** (List any fun things, dealing with feelings, job search, relationships, whatever!)

_____

_____

_____

_____

_____

# After the thirty days

So, you've finished the workbook. Congratulations are in order.

First assess where you are with your health. If you have made substantial progress, this certainly speaks to the efficacy of the mindbody approach with your disorder. The progress you've made should build upon itself and continue to grow. You can come back and reread your entries at any time, approaching them with a fresh perspective. You may even decide to continue keeping a journal, or even answering these questions a second time, in a blank notebook.

If you've made little or no progress with your condition, or gotten worse, it's time to reassess the situation. Ideally, its time for you be seen by a qualified physician, preferably mindbody-oriented. This might be a reexamination or perhaps a first visit. If the doctor finds nothing of concern, or no change in his original assessment, then you've got more work to do. You're an excellent candidate, perhaps, for a mindbody psychotherapist in your area. In addition, you should consider repeating the thirty-day cycle after a few days off and answering the questions again, perhaps in a separate notebook.

If you are still having a great deal of difficulty accepting your condition as psychosomatic or believing in the power of the mindbody connection, then reading or re-reading one of the books in the bibliography pertinent to this subject is appropriate. Dealing with your doubt intellectually and dealing with the emotional issues underlying your doubt is crucial. A good psychotherapist can be crucial to elucidating these factors.

Breaking the cycle of pain and brain takes some people a short time and others somewhat longer. If you are in the latter category, don't despair. This time course does not mean you won't be quite successful with this approach in the longer run. While your path may be longer, your commitment to begin the process, to look inside yourself for answers, and complete this thirty-day program, speaks forcefully to your ultimate success. Keep going…

# Bibliography

## Back Pain, TMS

Sarno, J., *Mind Over Back Pain*, Berkley Books, New York, 1986.

Sarno, J., *Healing Back Pain*, Warner Books, New York, 1991.

Sarno, J., *The MindBody Prescription*, Warner Books, New York, 1998.

Sarno, J, *The Divided Mind*, Harper Collins, New York, 2006

Schechter, D. *Think Away Your Pain*, MBM Publications. Los Angeles. 2014

Hanscomb, D. *Back in Control*, Vertus Press. Seattle. 2012

## Cancer

Siegel, B., *Love, Medicine, and Miracles*, Harper and Row, New York, 1986.

## Mind-body Connection

Moyers, B., *Healing and the Mind*, Doubleday, New York, 1993.

Ornstein, R. and Sobel, D., *Healthy Pleasures*, Addison-Wesley, 1989.

Weil, A. *Spontaneous Healing*, Knopf, New York, 1995.

Locke, S. and Colligan, D., *The Healer Within*, Penguin, New York, 1986.

## Rheumatology, Laughter as Healing

Cousins, N., *Anatomy of An Illness*, New York, Norton, 1979.

Cousins, N., *Healing Heart*, Avon books, 1983.

# Cardiac Problems

Friedman and Rosenman, *Type A Behavior and Your Heart*, Knopf, New York, 1984.

Ornish, D., *Reversing Heart Disease*, Ballantine Books, New York, 1990.

# Specific Emotions and Pain

Hay, L., *Heal Your Body*, Hay House, Carson, CA, 1988.

# Neurobiology of mind–body connection

Pert, C., *Molecules of Emotion*, Simon and Schuster, New York, 1997.

# Sociology of Pain and Chronic Fatigue/History

Shorter, E., *From Paralysis to Fatigue*, MacMillan, New York, 1992.

# Mindfulness, Meditation

Kabat-Zinn, J., *Wherever You Go There You Are*, Noetic Sciences, 1994.

# Biopsychosocial Philosophy

Engel, G., "The Need for a New Medical Model: A Challenge to Biomedicine", Science, 196: no. 4286, p.129-135, 1976.

# Appendix One—TMS Basics

Dr. John Sarno describes Tension Myositis Syndrome (or TMS) in great detail in four books—*Mind over Back Pain* (MOBP), *Healing Back Pain* (HBP), *Mindbody Prescription* (MP) and *Divided Mind* (DM). He named this diagnosis in the 1970's to refer to individuals with painful conditions of the back, neck and other areas of the skeleton. The Tension refers to emotional tension, the root cause, and muscle tension, the physical manifestation. Myositis refers to the fact that muscles are tender and sore on examination. Syndrome refers to the fact that the clinical manifestations of this condition are varied and can include back pain, neck pain, tingling, and other symptoms. Later on he preferred Tension Myoneural Syndrome, a more accurate term. Myoneural referring to muscles and nerves, areas of pain.

I sometimes use Distraction Pain Syndrome (DPS) in some of my own writing on this subject. (www.smi-MindBodyResearch.org). *Think Away Your Pain* was published in 2014 and attempts to update and clarify chronic pain. The subtitle, *"Your Brain is the Solution to Your Pain"* captures the essence and relates to the book's connection between scientific research in neuroscience and the clinical treatment of pain. The MindBody Syndrome is another term for this condition or syndrome. Psychophysiologic Disorder, as well. (PPD). Neuroplastic pain, yet another.

Individuals with TMS often have tender points on examination, frequently have had other psychosomatic conditions in their medical history and have a characteristic personality type. I use the term "Type T" (akin to Type "A" for heart disease) to refer to the perfectionism, self-criticism, and responsibility that these individuals exhibit. These personality features, many of which are morally or professionally desirable, create a great deal of internal pressure or tension that is often expressed in physical symptoms, i.e. psychosomatic disorders. (See Chapter 2, MP or Chapter 2, HBP, Chapter 3, THINK)

Individuals with this constellation of personality characteristics, past history, and physical findings are often treated for back sprains, bulging discs, and the like with temporary success and the inevitable recurrence of symptoms. Symptoms not uncommonly shift to another part of the body and from side to side. Individuals improve when informed of the true nature of their symptoms, educated about the painful but benign nature of the condition, and encouraged to think psychologically rather than structurally about their pain (see Chapter 4 HBP or Chapter 9, MP, Chapter 10, THINK). While often difficult for individuals to believe, an awareness of the connection between emotions and the pain is frequently sufficient for the pain to resolve. For deeper-rooted emotional issues, a more prolonged self-examination and/or focused psychotherapy is remarkably effective in treating the pain and enabling the patient to live a more active lifestyle.

# Appendix Two— Finding a MindBody Practitioner

I use the term mindbody throughout this workbook. However, a mindbody doctor is hard to find and harder to classify. Many primary care physicians have a wholistic emphasis. An individual trained in pain management may combine up to date physical and imaging skills along with a psychological mindset.

Doctors who have trained with or been cured by the work of Dr. John Sarno may be a good place to start in looking for a mindbody cure. Currently, there are a few dozen of these individuals nationally or internationally. Many are mentioned on the web site www. mindbodymedicine.com. The ability to be knowledgeable in the conventional diagnosis or treatment of a condition is important, as well as the specialized knowledge of TMS diagnosis and treatment.

Ideally, a mindbody practitioner should be psychologically aware himself (herself). He may have a background or exposure to psychology or psychiatric diagnosis. This mindbody approach is, in the truest sense, wholistic. It is alternative only in the sense that mainstream medicine is not mindbody in outlook.

If a TMS practitioner is not available in your area, seek out a well-trained doctor who also comes recommended by others. If your psychosomatic problem is not back pain, find a doctor who specializes in that problem or a good primary care physician. Preferably, look for an open-minded, empathic individual open to psychological aspects of illness. Unfortunately, this is not that simple, as well. If all else fails, settle with someone with good technical training and expertise who can exclude serious pathology (cancer, fractures, infection, etc.).

Ask the doctor if a conservative program is suitable. If he agrees, begin the mindbody program, along with other treatments he may recommend. If the doctor advises surgery, get a second opinion in your area. If necessary, get a third opinion. Some conditions require surgery—be sure to have the best surgeon you can find and get the least surgery that can treat the condition effectively. If the doctor agrees, a purely psychological program of devoting yourself to the Workbook for thirty days, deferring other treatments, is often most effective. However, the Workbook can certainly be combined with other treatments that alleviate pain, increase flexibility, and improve strength.

Common sense should prevail. Your local doctor is your medical advisor. If what he says makes sense to you, then follow it wholeheartedly. If you're not getting better, seek other opinions. A good primary care doctor who specializes in family practice or internal medicine is often the best person with whom to talk about wholistic medicine. They can also be your advocate or interpreter of specialist's recommendations for your care. Finally, they are usually the best judges of whether your psychological status requires psychotherapy, antidepressant medications, antianxiety medications, or a combination of these.

Psychiatrists and psychologists often suffer from the same mind/body split as the rest of the medical field. Try to find one who is familiar with TMS, open to reading the book, or adept with psychosomatic disorders. Explain to them that you don't want to learn how to cope with the pain, you want to understand how your emotions may be causing or contributing to it. If they are not open to this concept, seek out another "shrink."

Finally, while I enjoy receiving emails and letters, I cannot diagnose nor treat without a face-to-face consultation and examination. Therefore, you will need to trust that your local doctors are doing the best that they can for you. You are in charge of whom you see and what treatments you accept. They are there to advise and care for you.

**Good luck.**

**David Schechter, MD**

| | |
|---|---|
| **TMS Information, Book, DVD, Audible Book** | **www.MindBodyMedicine.com** |
| **Office Consultations—(310) 836-2225** | **www.SchechterMD.com** |
| **2014 Book—*Think Away Your Pain*** | **www.ThinkAwayPain.us** |

**All publications available on Amazon.com (Kindle, Audible), some on nook and itunes.**

**MINDBODY
MEDICINE
PUBLICATIONS**

# About the Author

David Schechter, MD is a board-certified family medicine/sports medicine physician who has explored the mindbody connection in his medical training, clinical practice and research for over thirty five years. Inspired by the writings of George Engel, MD about the biopsychosocial model of disease and the work of John Sarno, MD on Tension Myositis Syndrome, he has incorporated an integrated mind-body approach into his unique clinical practice.

Over the last twenty-five plus years, Dr. Schechter has further focused on the treatment of back pain, neck pain, headaches, RSI and other disorders, using a mindbody approach. The essence has been to teach patients not to fear their pain and to heal by acknowledging and connecting the pain to the underlying emotional issues in their lives. Dr. Schechter has helped many thousands of patients from all over the United States, from Canada, Mexico, Europe, the Middle East, and as far as Australia and Hong Kong who have utilized his unique treatment program.

Dr. Schechter has had an academic appointment at the USC School of Medicine and has taught medical students and residents. He has lectured at medical conferences and meetings. His book: **Think Away Your Pain** (2014) offers clear, user-friendly explanations, more treatment focus, and more science for those who are interested. For information, podcasts, or to order items, go to www.MindBodyMedicine.com or review www.SchechterMD.com.

Dr. Schechter lives in Los Angeles with his wife and has two sons. His office is in Culver City (310-836-2225). Dr. Schechter was the Principal Investigator of the Seligman Medical Institute, a non-profit foundation dedicated to furthering the understanding of TMS and other mindbody disorders. He is currently Treasurer of the non-profit Psycho Physiologic Disorders Association (www.ppdassociation.org)

Made in the USA
Las Vegas, NV
02 January 2023

64582747R00059